BOOK ONE

Primary Analogies

Critical and Creative Thinking

Educators Publishing Service, Inc.
Cambridge and Toronto

ACKNOWLEDGMENTS

Dr. Frederick J. Stokley, Superintendent of Schools in Ridgewood, New Jersey, initiated the idea of publishing Ridgewood curriculum. He hoped that Ridgewood could contribute to American education by sharing material that has proved particularly stimulating and effective in the Ridgewood schools.

Maria Sweeney, Project Manager for Curriculum Publications, organized and supervised the team that developed the primary analogies material. She worked closely with the publisher as both a consultant and a facilitator.

Joan Hartmann, Secretary, provided organizational support for the project.

About the Authors, page 40

Cover art by Hyo-Won Lee

Cover design by Joyce Weston

 Printed in the U.S.A.

ISBN 0-8388-2283-5

November 2000 Printing

Draw a line from each picture in the Picture Bank to a picture below that is similar to it.

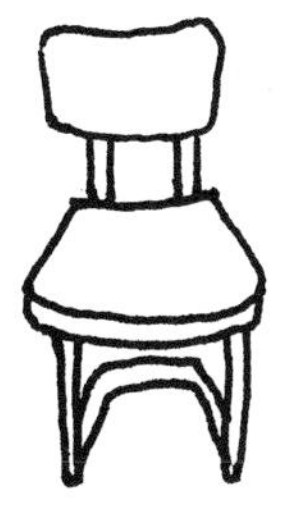

The Picture Bank has pictures of things that have something to do with Halloween, Thanksgiving, and birthdays. Circle each picture and draw a line from it to the box it goes with.

Look at the two pictures in each box. Circle something on one picture that is similar to something on the other picture. There may be more than one thing that is similar. The first one is started for you.

1.

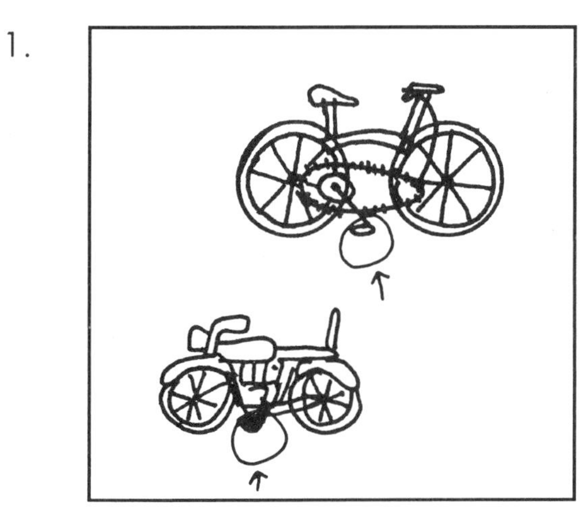

2.

3.

4.

5.

6.

The two circles below overlap, making three sections. Draw a line from the animal in the Picture Bank to the section it goes in. Section A is for farm animals and Section B is for circus animals. Section C is for any animals that have four legs, so it will have both farm animals and circus animals — any animals that have four legs.

A = farm animals
B = circus animals
C = four-legged animals

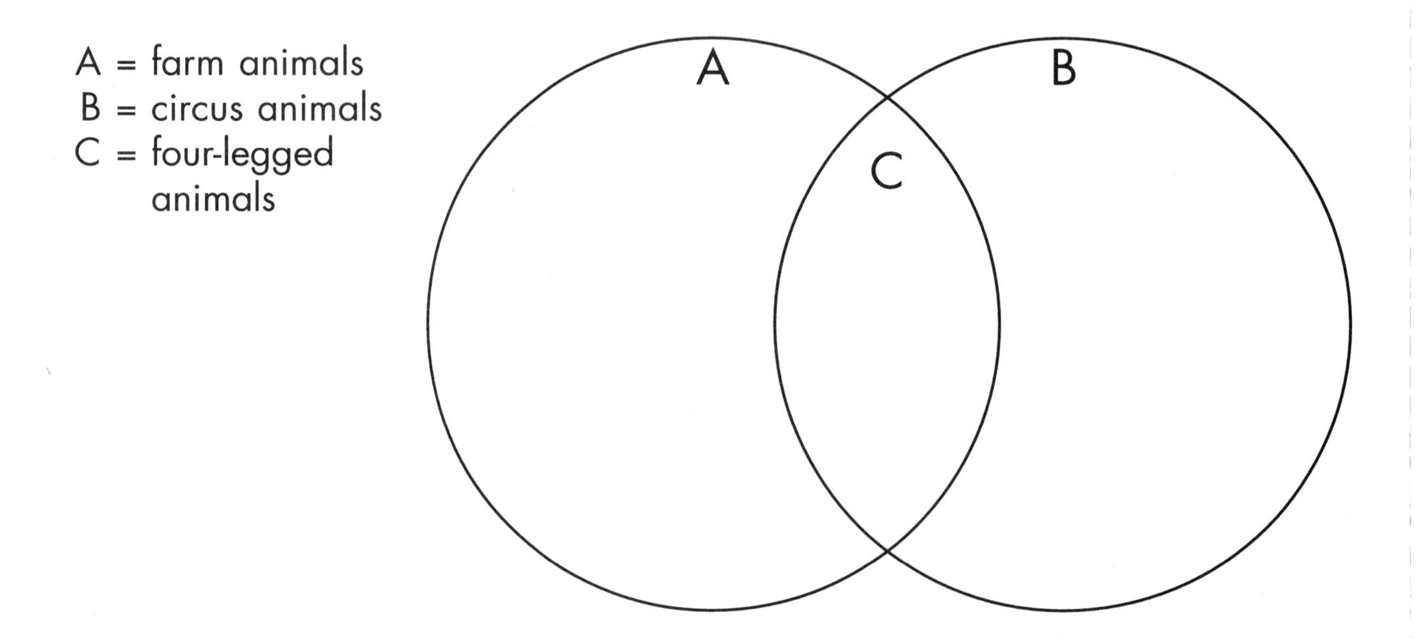

In each box, a line connects two pictures that go together. Draw a line to connect two other pictures in the box that go together in the same way.

In each box, a line connects two pictures that go together. Draw a line to connect two other pictures in the box that go together in the same way.

In each box, a line connects two pictures that go together. Draw a line to connect two other pictures in the box that go together in the same way.

In each box, a line connects two pictures that go together. Draw a line to connect two other pictures in the box that go together in the same way.

In each box, a line connects two pictures that go together. Draw a line to connect two other pictures in the box that go together in the same way.

In each box, a line connects two pictures that go together. Draw a line to connect two other pictures in the box that go together in the same way.

In each box, a line connects two pictures that go together. Draw a line to connect two other pictures in the box that go together in the same way.

In each box, a line connects two pictures that go together. Draw a line to connect two other pictures in the box that go together in the same way.

In each box, a line connects two pictures that go together. Draw a line to connect two other pictures in the box that go together in the same way.

In each box, a line connects two pictures that go together. Draw a line to connect two other pictures in the box that go together in the same way.

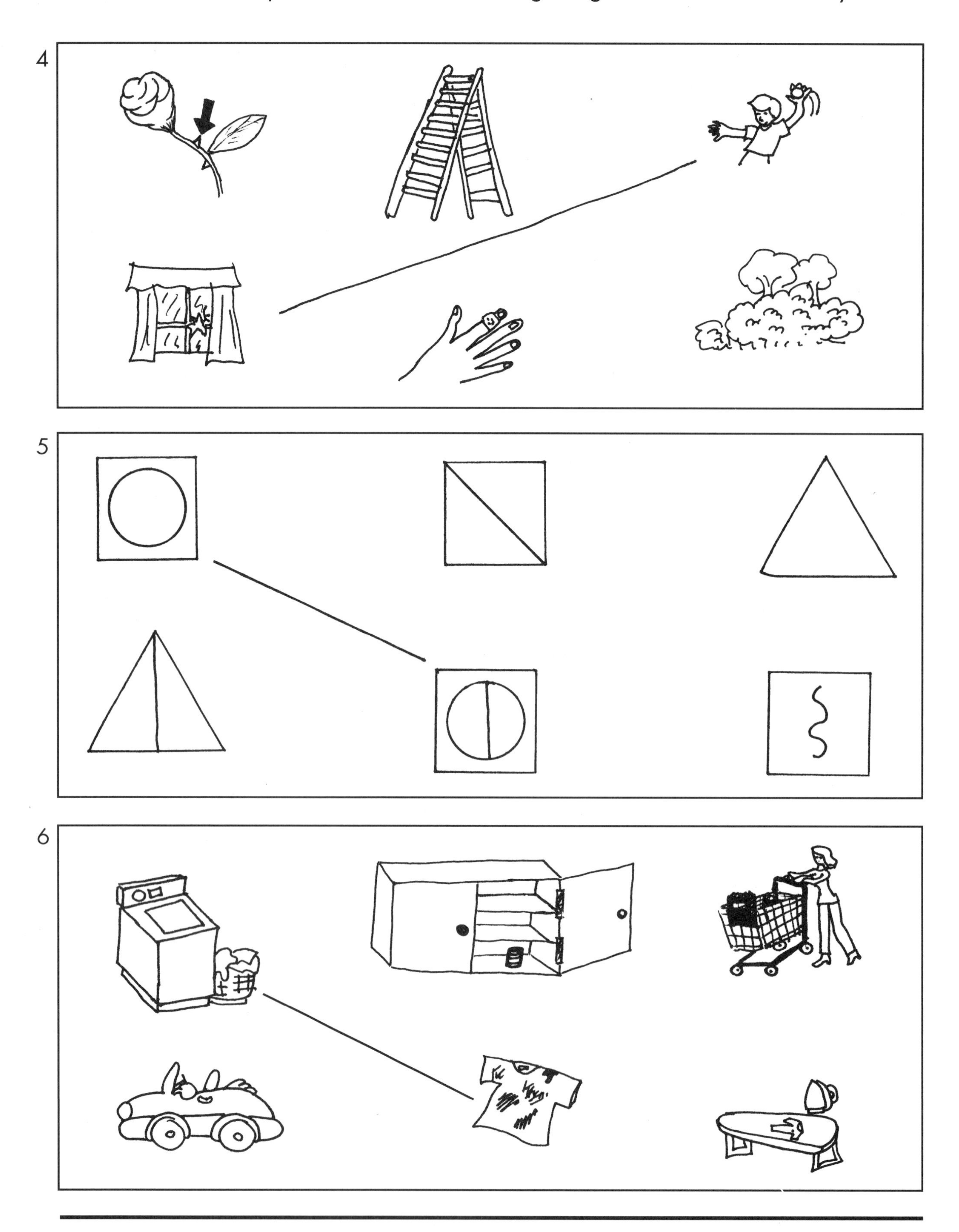

Find an item in the Answer Box to put in the empty box so both pairs go together in the same way. Circle the item in the box.

Find an item in the Answer Box to put in the empty box so both pairs go together in the same way. Circle the item in the box.

Find an item in the Answer Box to put in the empty box so both pairs go together in the same way. Circle the item in the box.

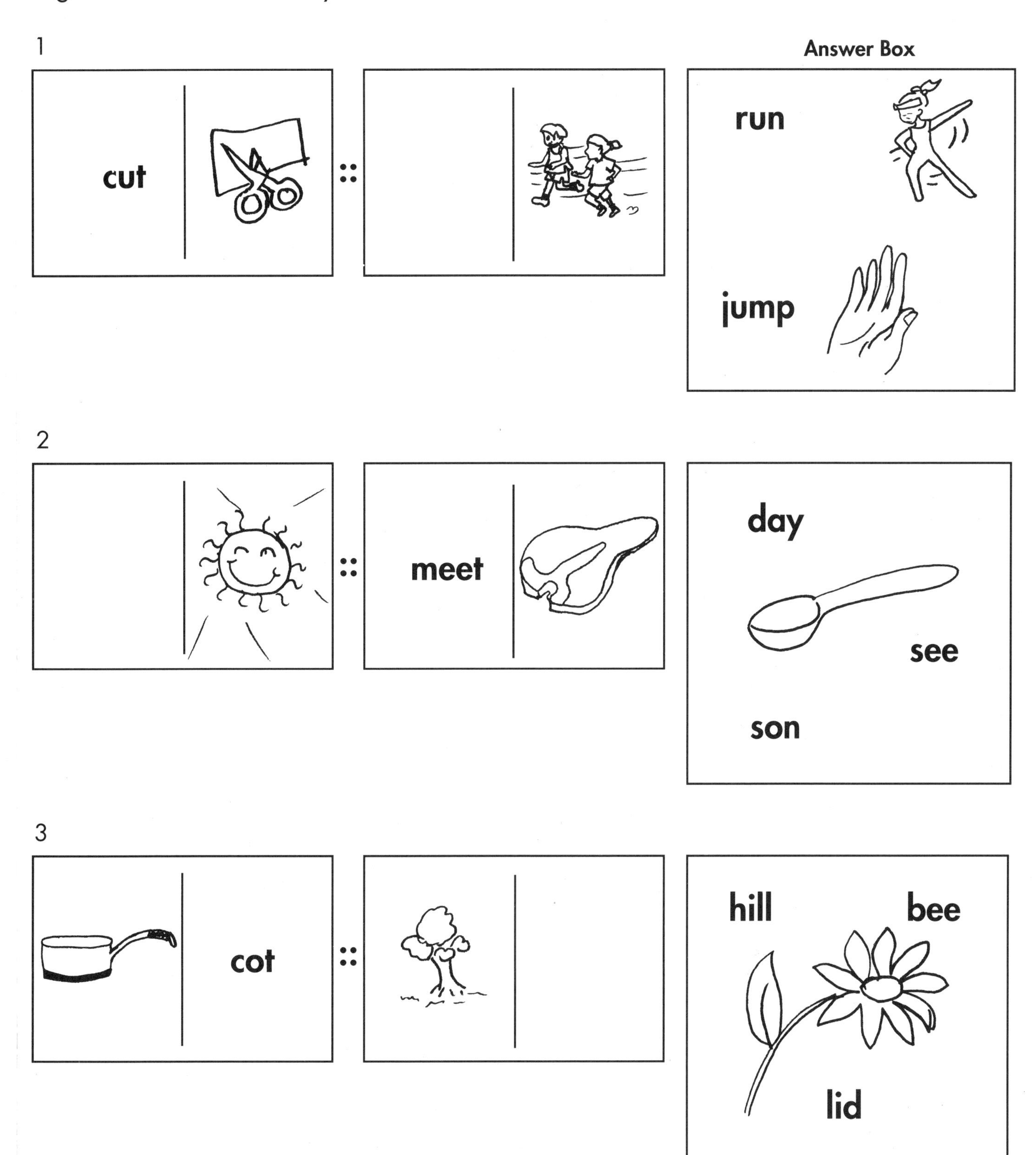

Find an item in the Answer Box to put in the empty box so both pairs go together in the same way. Circle the item in the box.

Find an item in the Answer Box to put in the empty box so both pairs go together in the same way. Circle the item in the box.

Find an item in the Answer Box to put in the empty box so both pairs go together in the same way. Circle the item in the box.

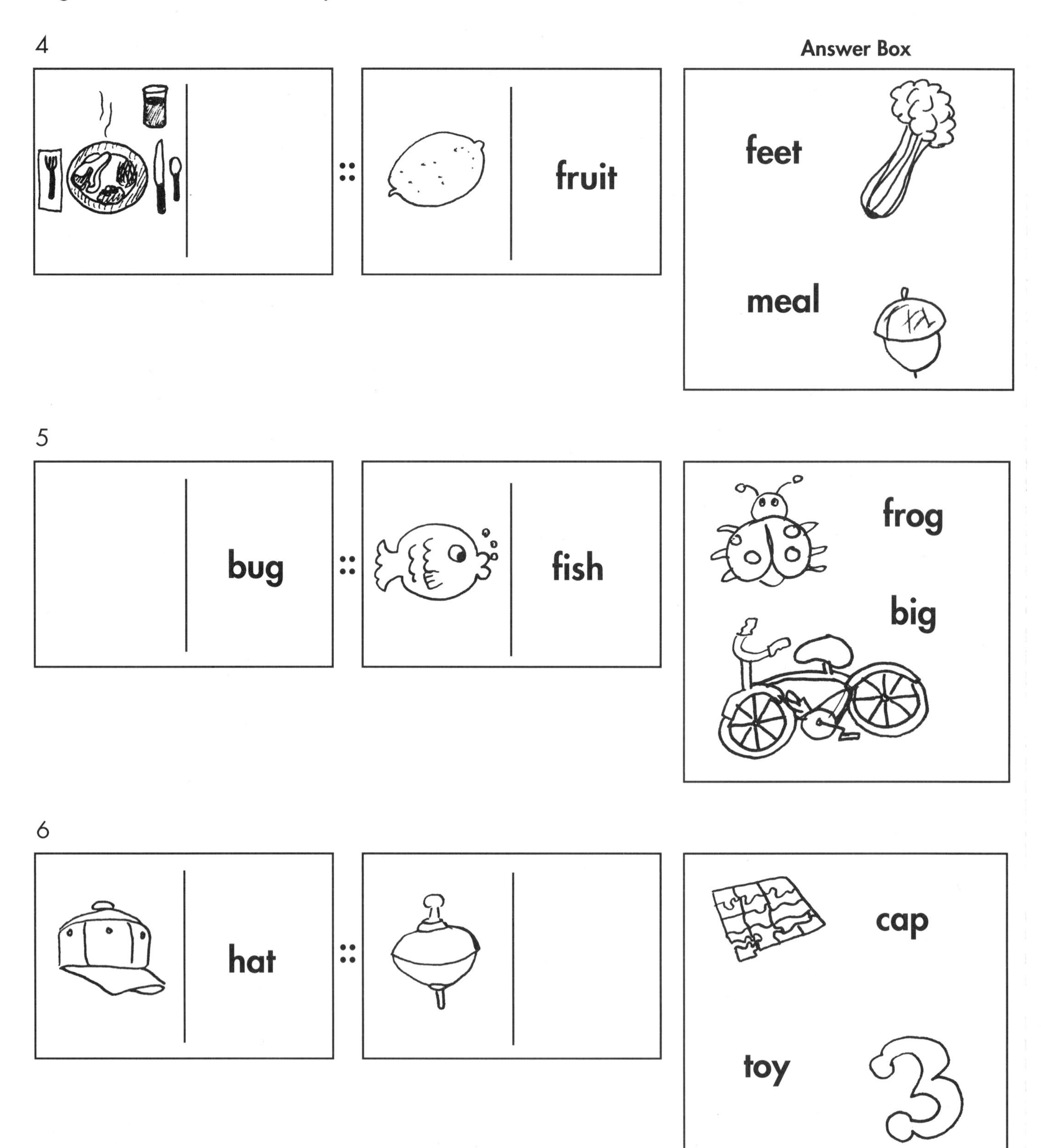

Find an item in the Answer Box to put in the empty box so both pairs go together in the same way. Circle the item in the box.

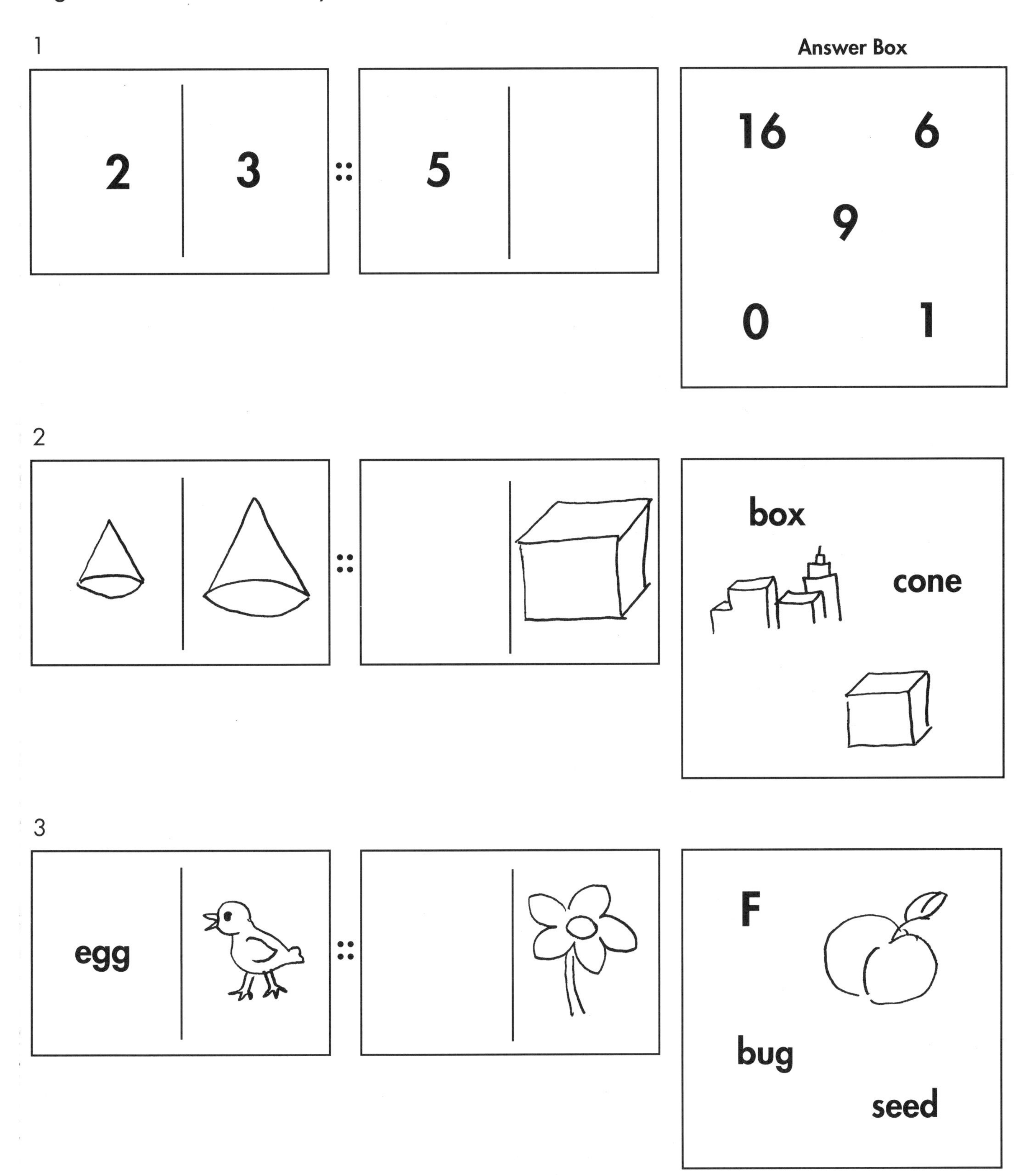

Find an item in the Answer Box to put in the empty box so both pairs go together in the same way. Circle the item in the box.

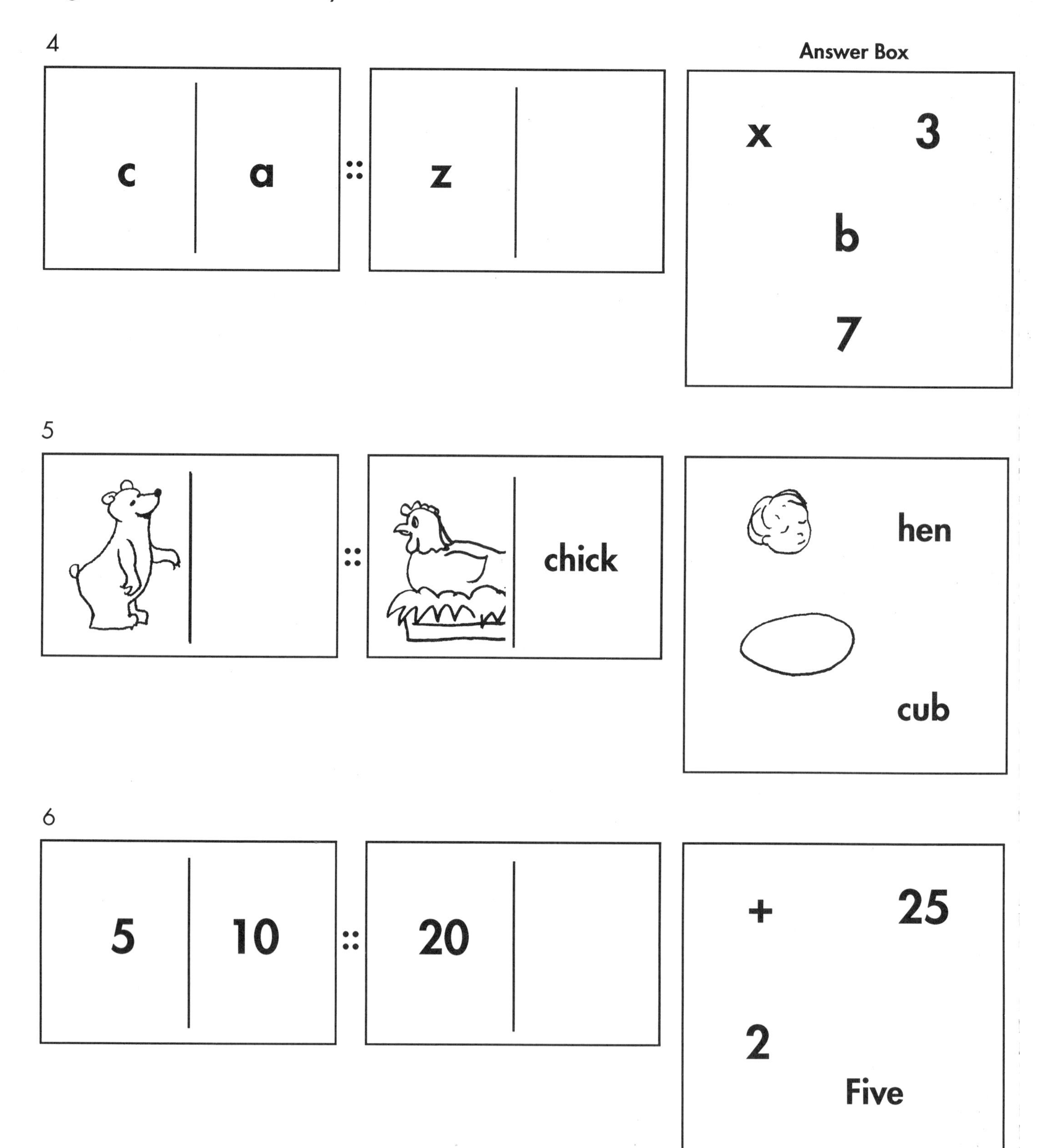

Find an item in the Answer Box to put in the empty box so both pairs go together in the same way. Circle the item in the box.

Find an item in the Answer Box to put in the empty box so both pairs go together in the same way. Circle the item in the box.

Find an item in the Answer Box to put in the empty box so both pairs go together in the same way.

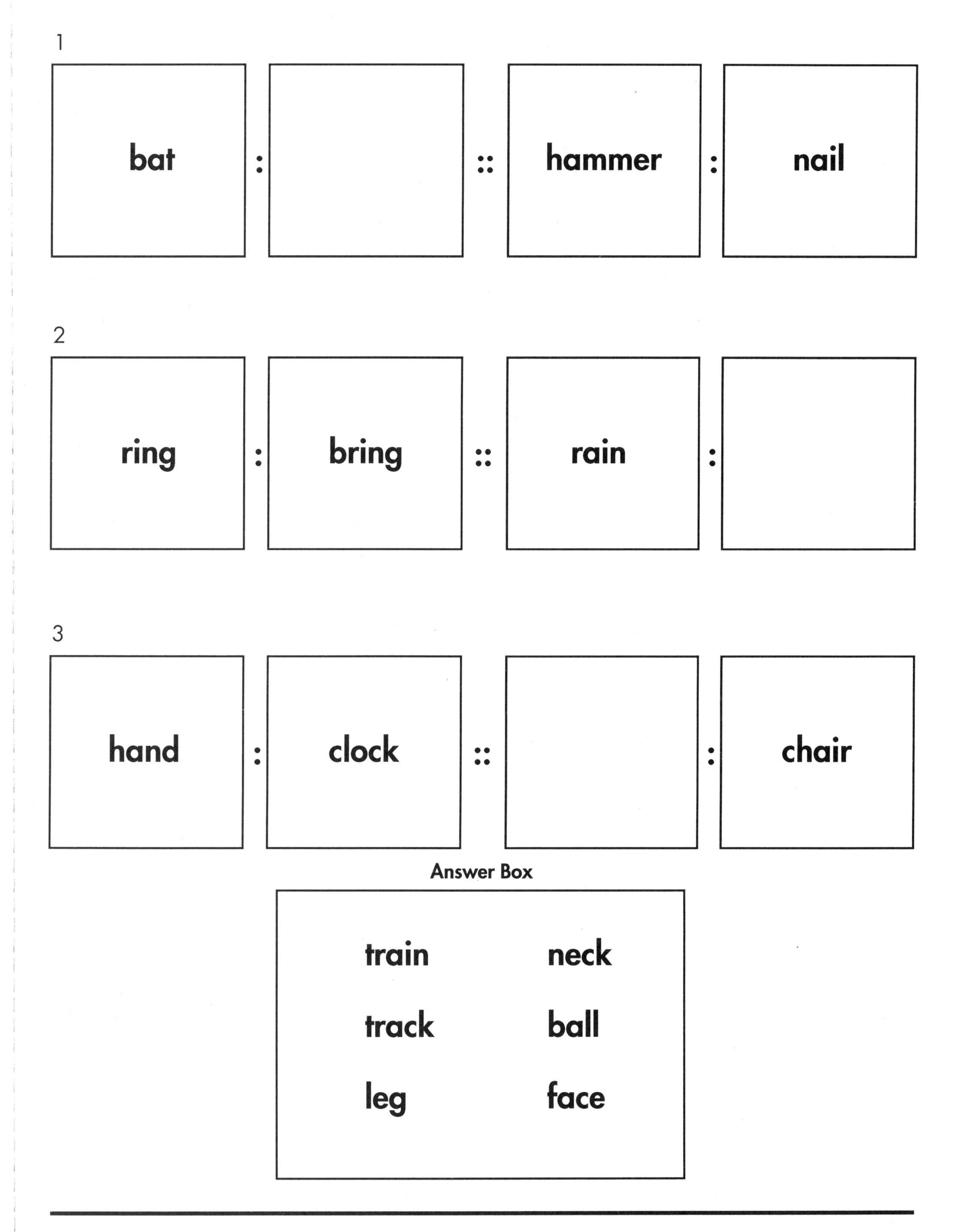

Find an item in the Answer Box to put in the empty box so both pairs go together in the same way.

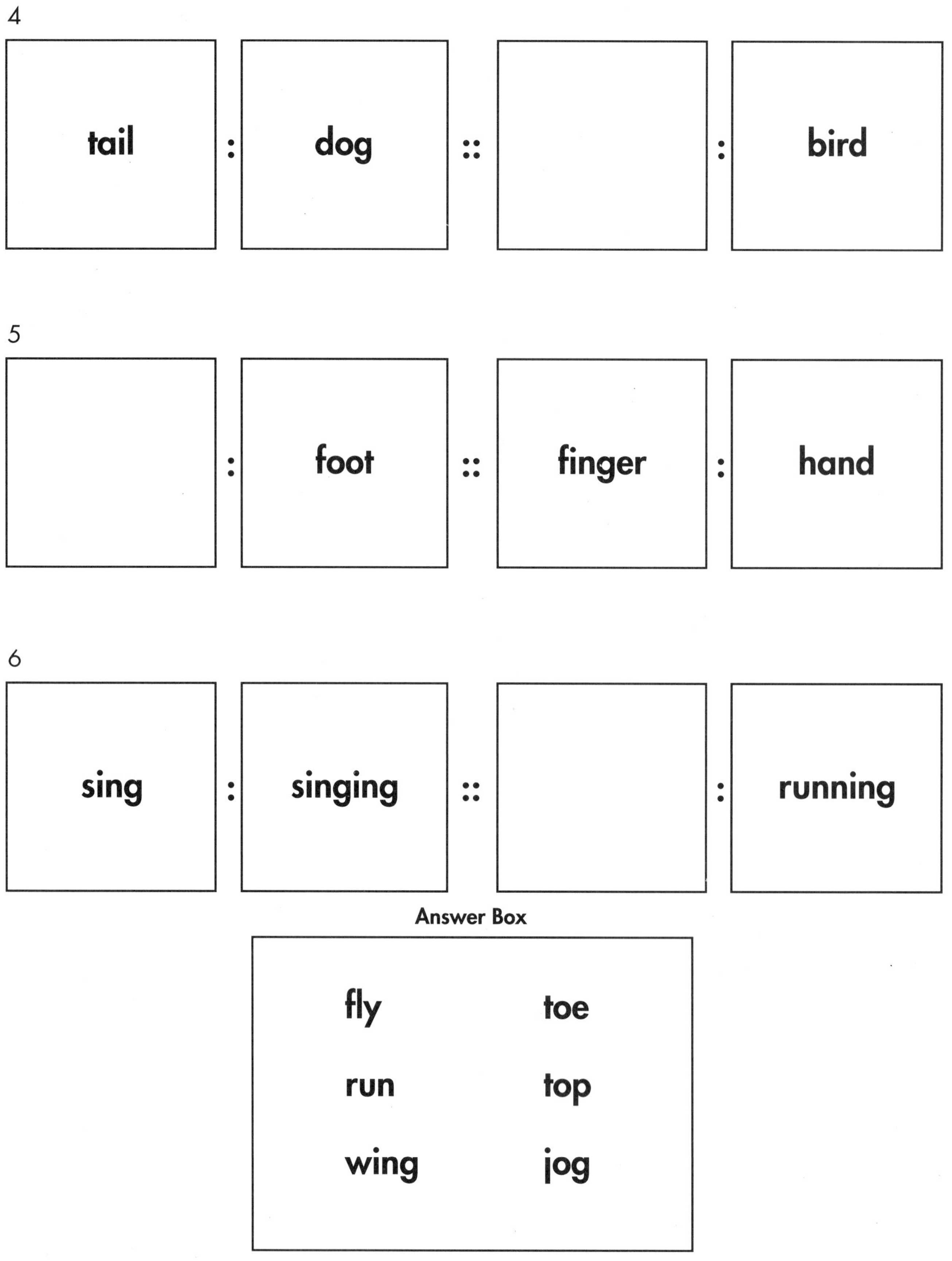

Find an item in the Answer Box to put in the empty box so both pairs go together in the same way.

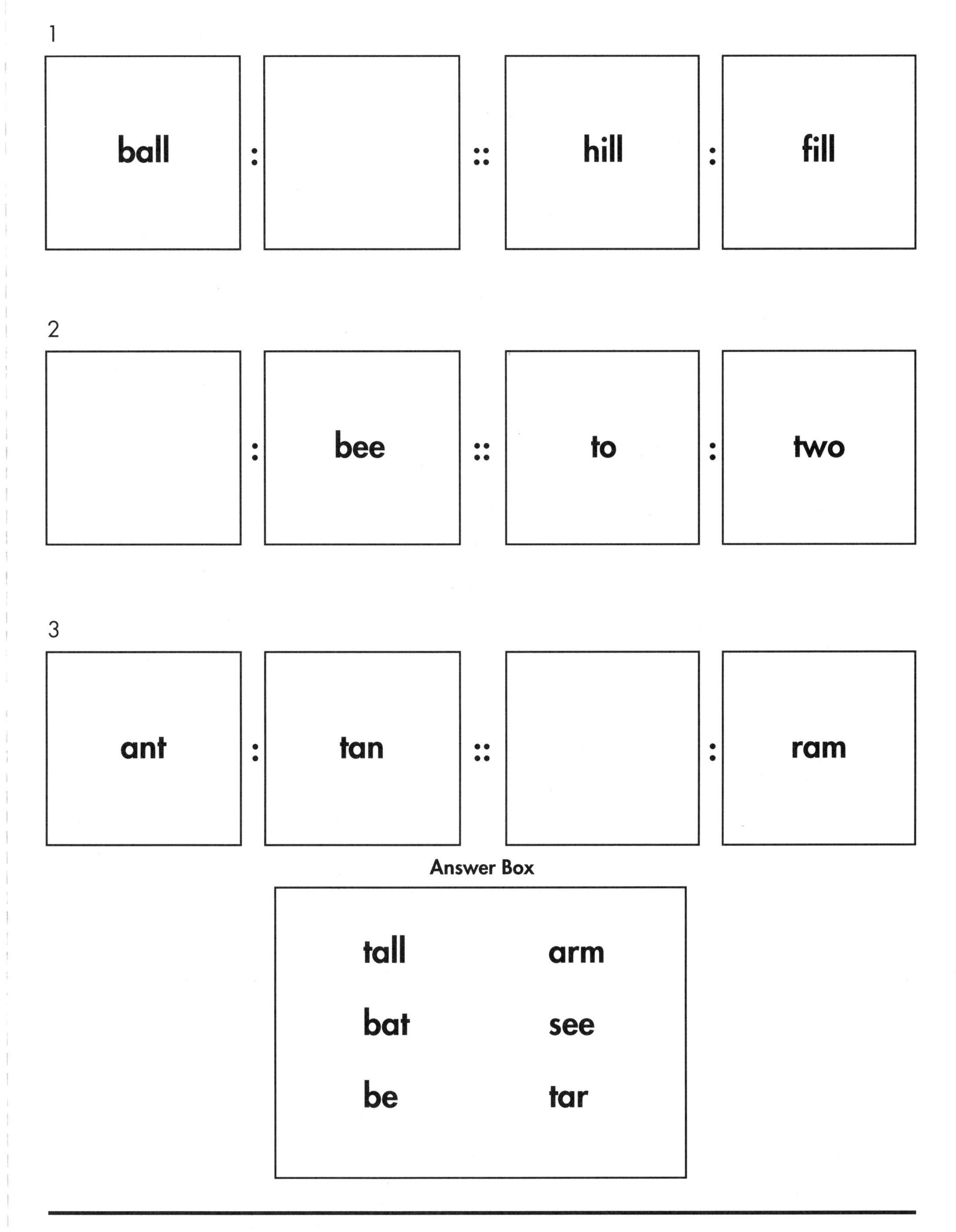

Find an item in the Answer Box to put in the empty box so both pairs go together in the same way.

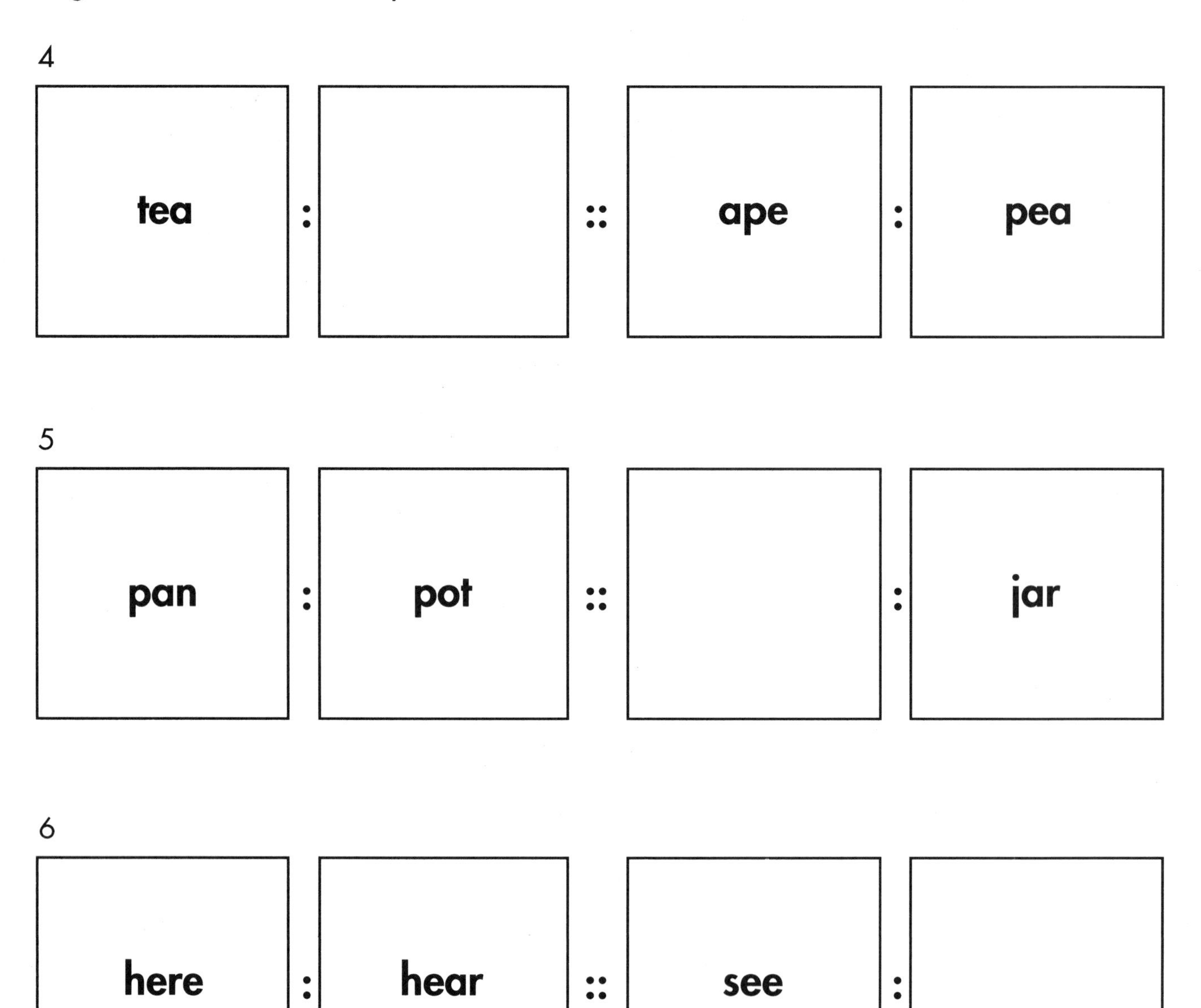

Answer Box

jug	cup
look	eat
sea	jam

Find an item in the Answer Box to put in the empty box so both pairs go together in the same way.

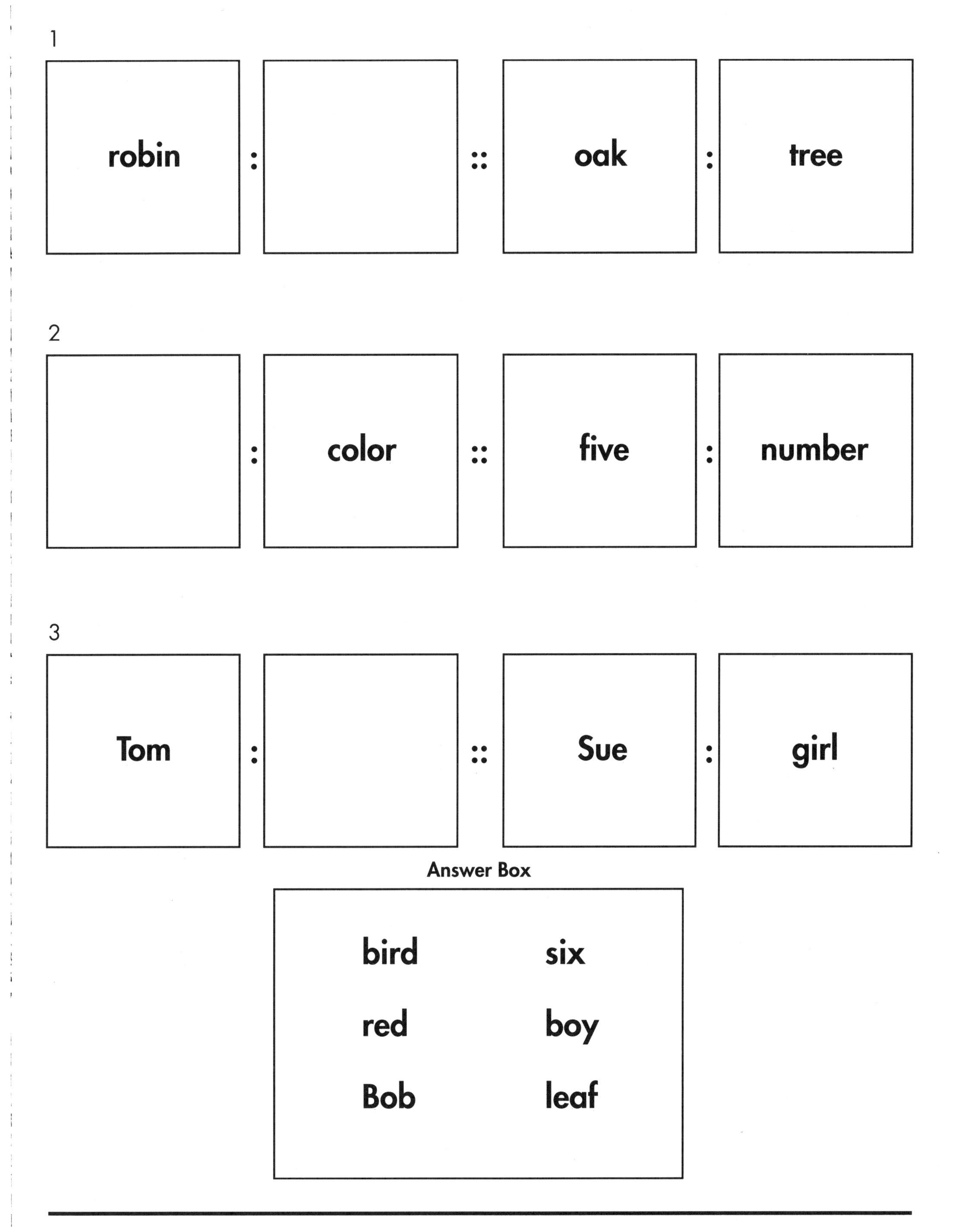

Find an item in the Answer Box to put in the empty box so both pairs go together in the same way.

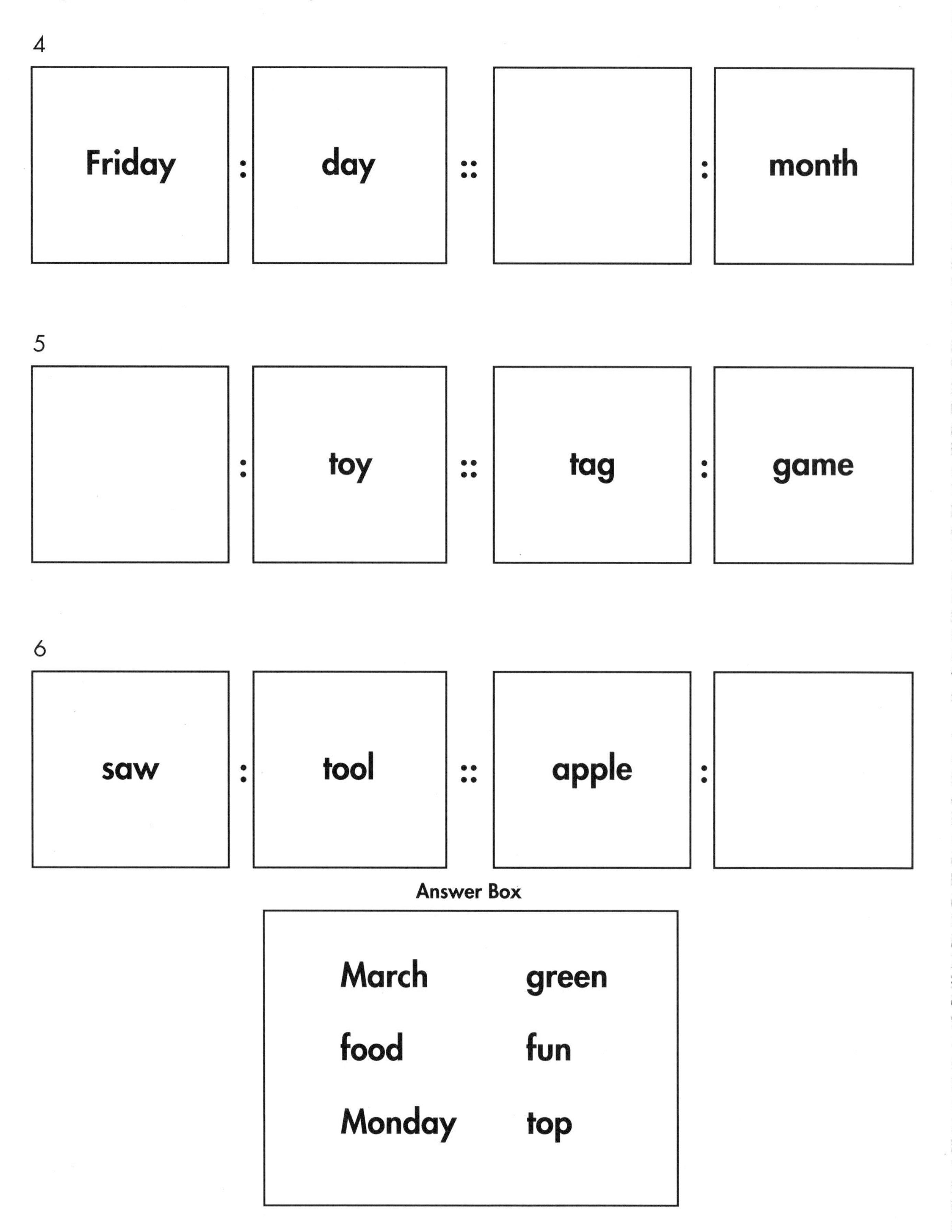

Find an item in the Answer Box to put in the empty box so both pairs go together in the same way.

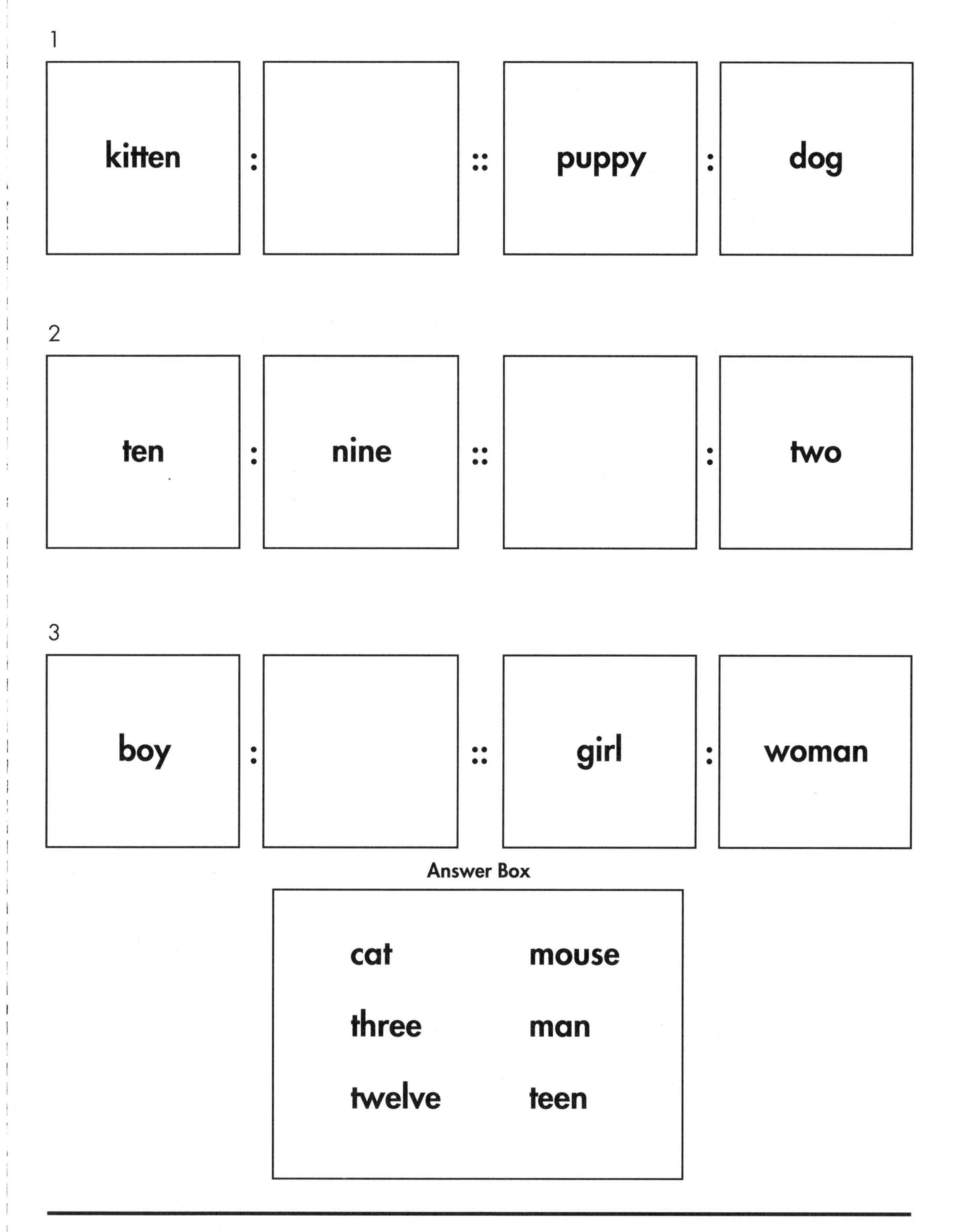

Find an item in the Answer Box to put in the empty box so both pairs go together in the same way.

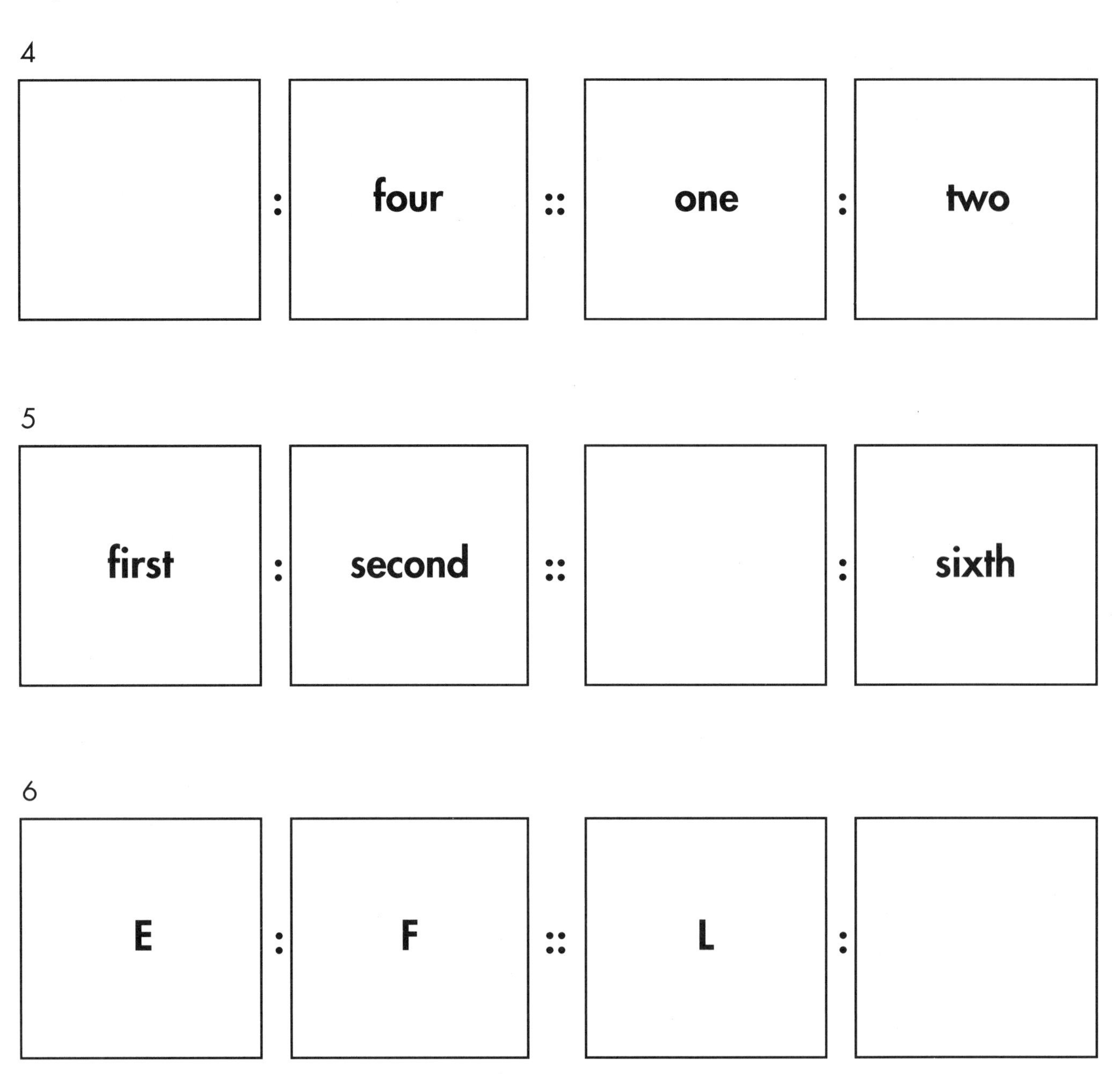

Answer Box

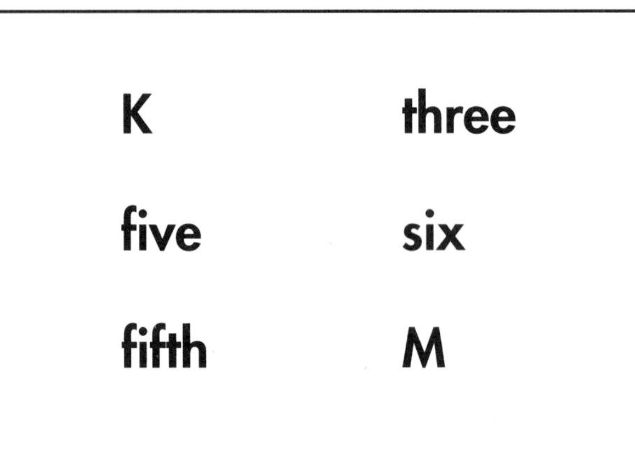

Find an item in the Answer Box to put in the empty box so both pairs go together in the same way.

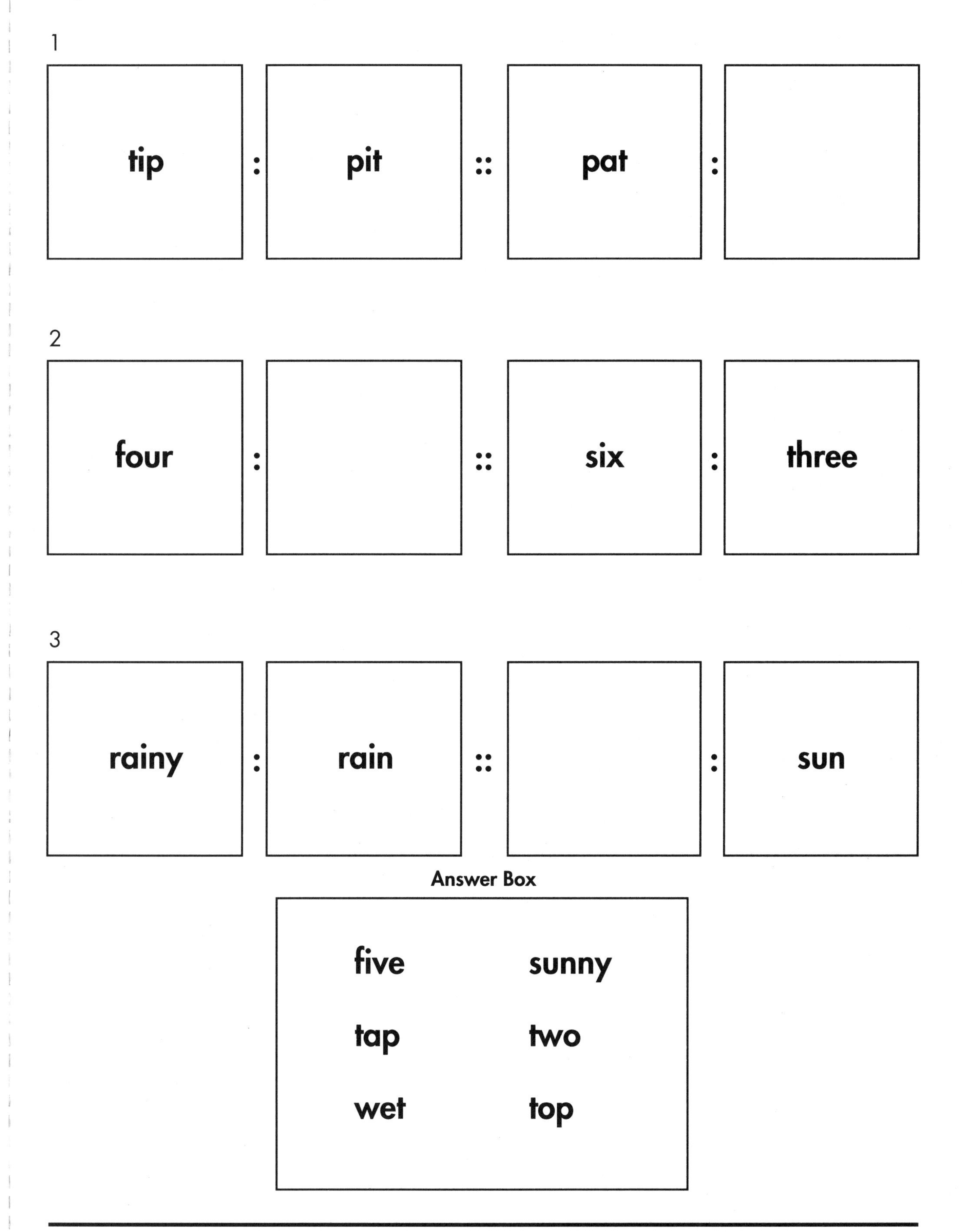

Find an item in the Answer Box to put in the empty box so both pairs go together in the same way.

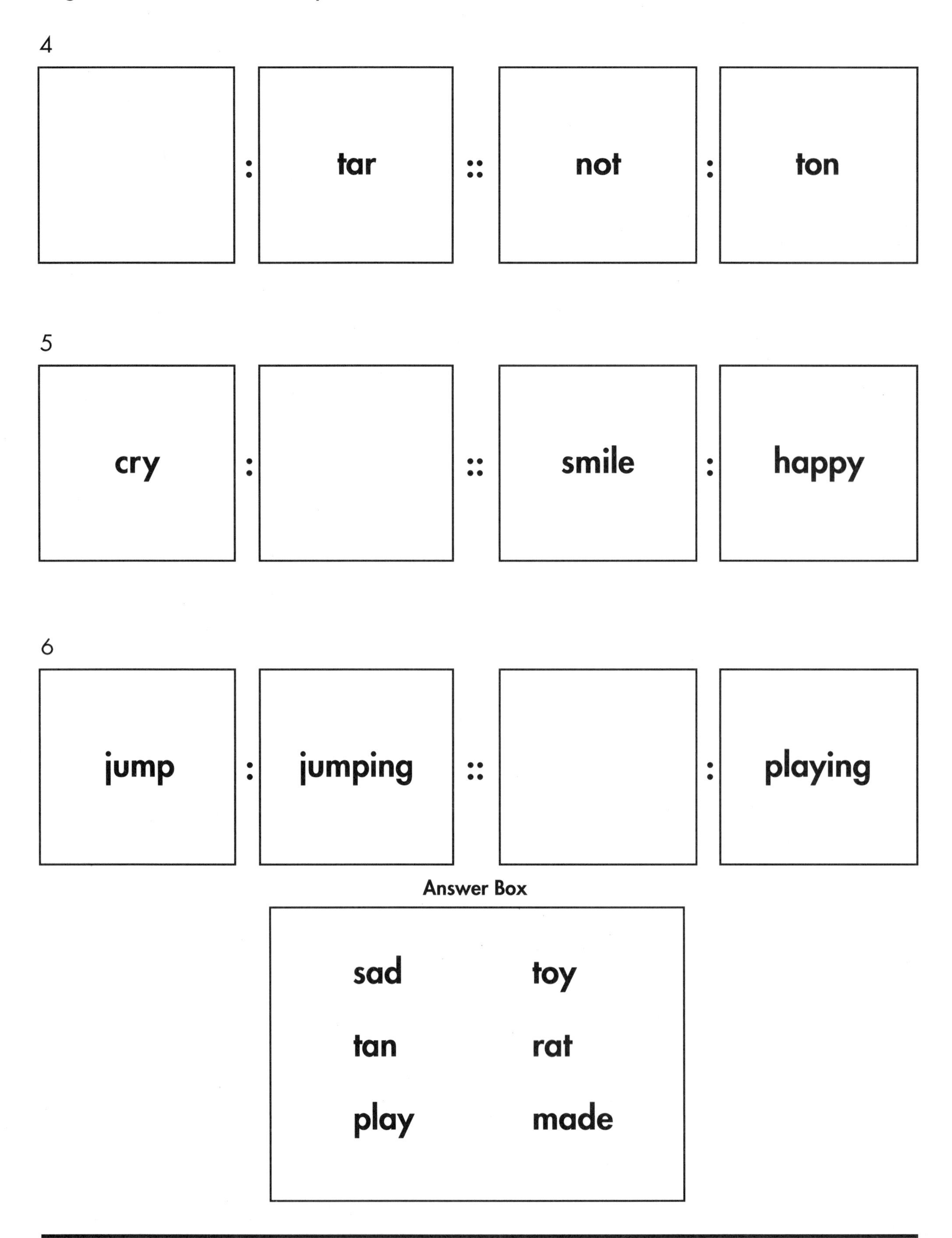

Answer Box

sad	toy
tan	rat
play	made

All-Stars. Make up your own analogies! Find two items in the Answer Box that go together in some way. Then find two other items in the box that go together in the same way. Write the analogy on the line. One is done for you.

Answer Box

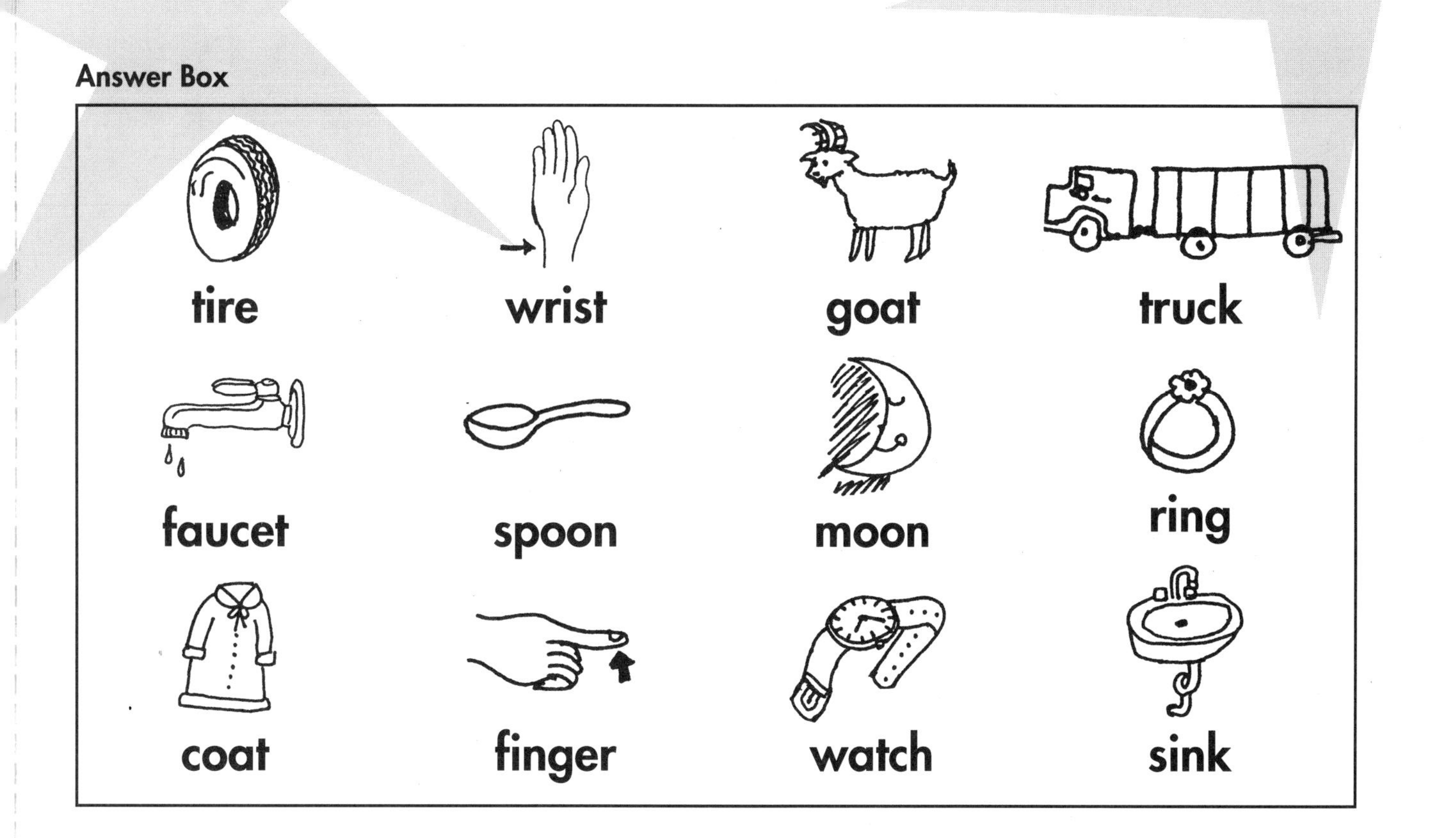

1. Watch is to wrist as ring is to finger.

2. ____

3. ____

All-Stars. Make up your own analogies! Find two items in the Answer Box that go together in some way. Then find two other items in the box that go together in the same way. Write the analogy on the line.

Answer Box

1. ______________________________

2. ______________________________

3. ______________________________

All-Stars. Make up your own analogies! Find two items in the Answer Box that go together in some way. Then find two other items in the box that go together in the same way. Write the analogy on the line.

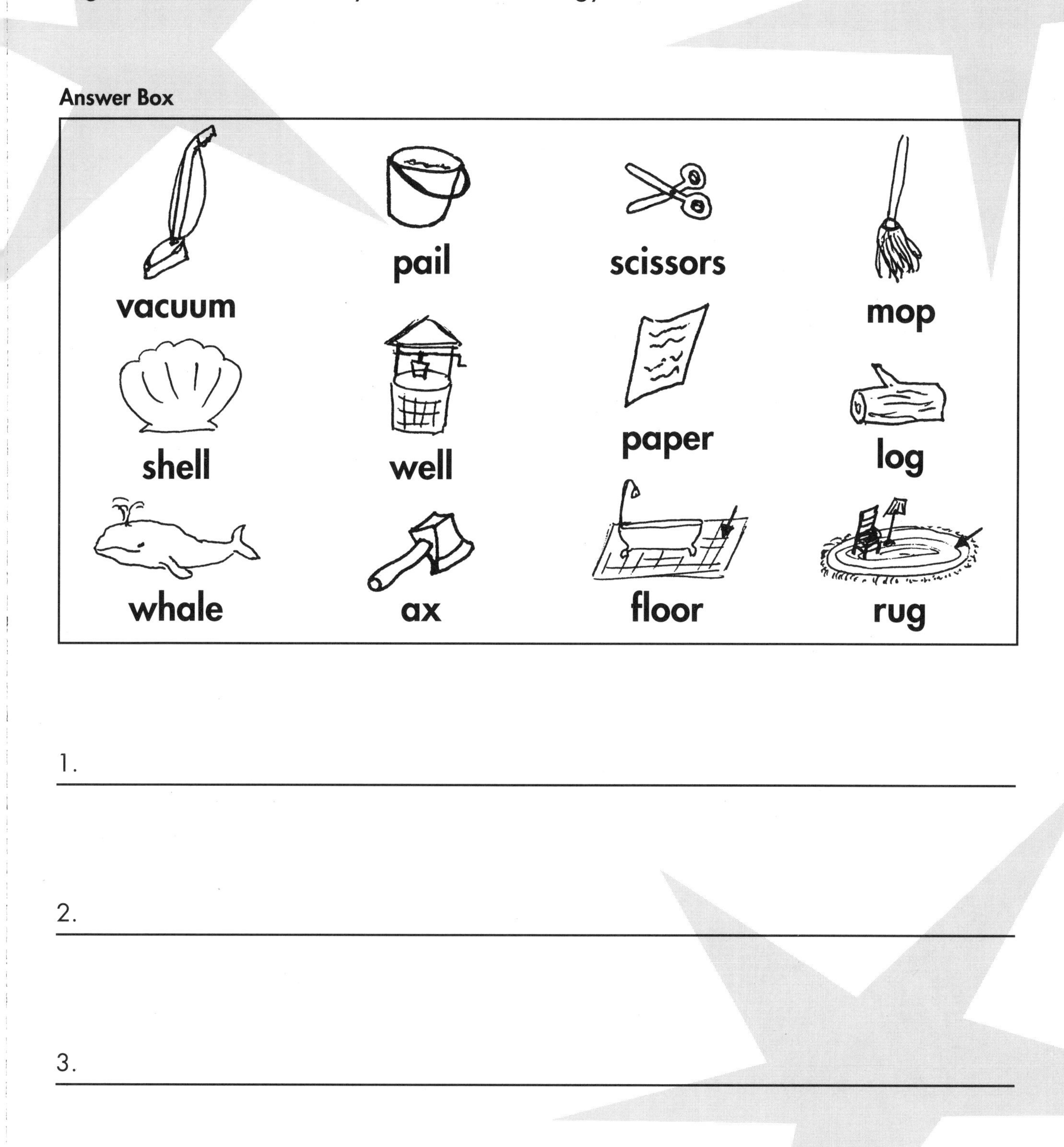

1. ______________________________

2. ______________________________

3. ______________________________

All-Stars. Make up your own analogies! Find two items in the Answer Box that go together in some way. Then find two other items in the box that go together in the same way. Write the analogy on the line.

Answer Box

1. ______________________________

2. ______________________________

3. ______________________________

All-Stars. Make up your own analogies! Find two items in the Answer Box that go together in some way. Then find two other items in the box that go together in the same way. Write the analogy on the line.

Answer Box

head	sleep	foot	red
chair	shoe	zoo	sit
orange	hat	pig	carrot
farm	beet	bed	zebra

1. ______________________________

2. ______________________________

3. ______________________________

ABOUT THE AUTHORS AND ILLUSTRATOR

Gae Brunner, a teacher for over twenty years, teaches fourth and fifth grade in Ridgewood. She has a masters degree in reading and has been a reading specialist and resource room teacher. She is an author of the district social studies test that emphasizes analogies related to content.

Jean Schoenlank teaches fifth grade in Ridgewood, where she has worked on curriculum, particularly on problem-solving projects. For several years she was editor of a districtwide professional newsletter. She has an Ed.M. from Harvard University.

Marianne Williams is the principal of an elementary school in Ridgewood. A teacher for over twenty-five years, she has a masters degree in administration and supervision, and developed the in-service program for the district. She worked on the district social studies and science tests that evaluate concept development in the subject areas through analogies, verbal reasoning, sequences, and memory.

Terri Wiss teaches fifth grade. She has a masters degree in learning disabilities and has taught special education and third through seventh grades for more than thirty years.

Illustrator **Hyo-Won Lee** is fourteen years old and attended school in Ridgewood. She returned to Seoul, South Korea, in the summer of 1995, but expects to return to the United States in a few years. Hyo began to draw at the age of three. She would like to be an artist or a cartoonist when she grows up.